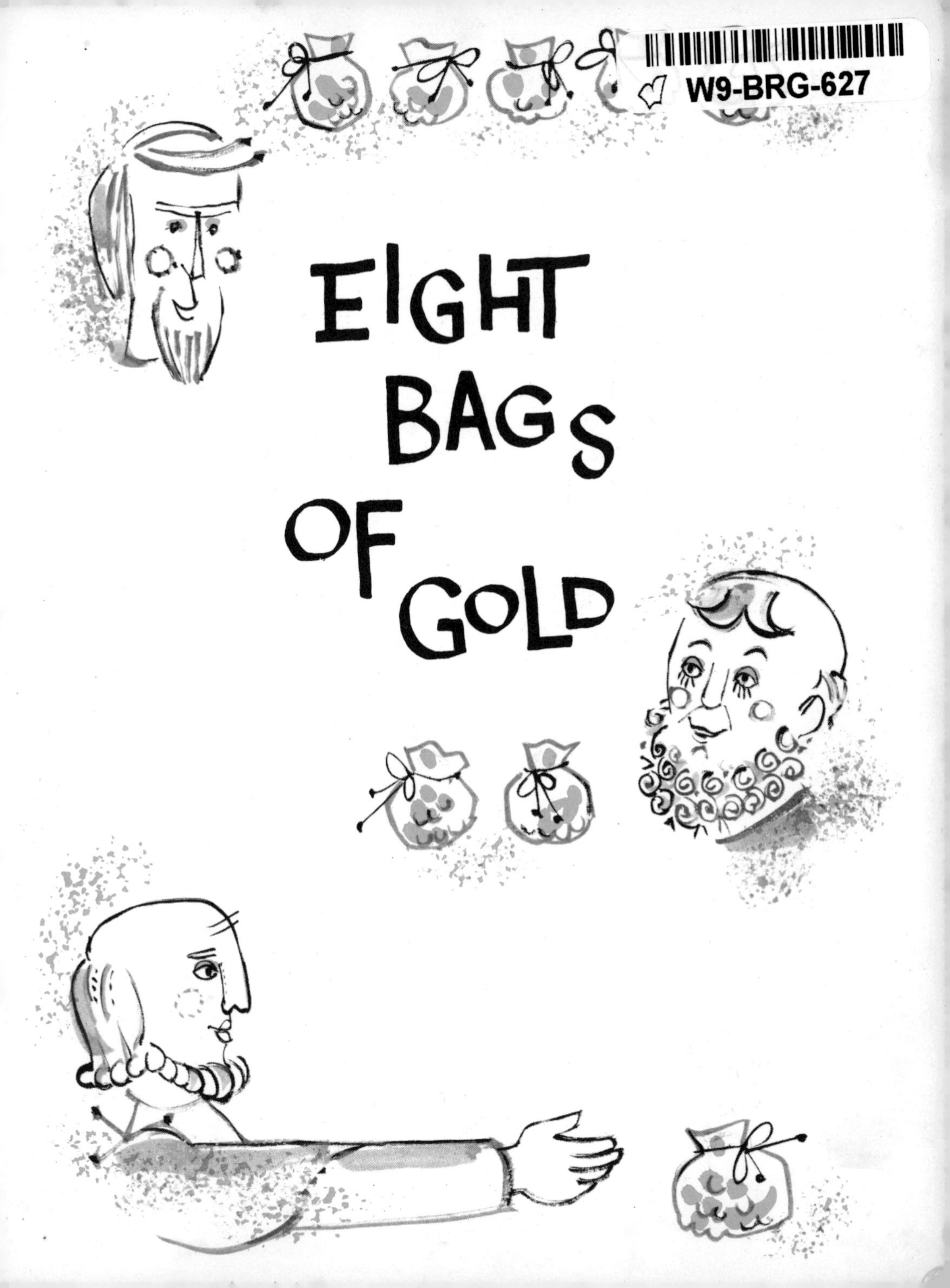
EIGHT BAGS OF GOLD

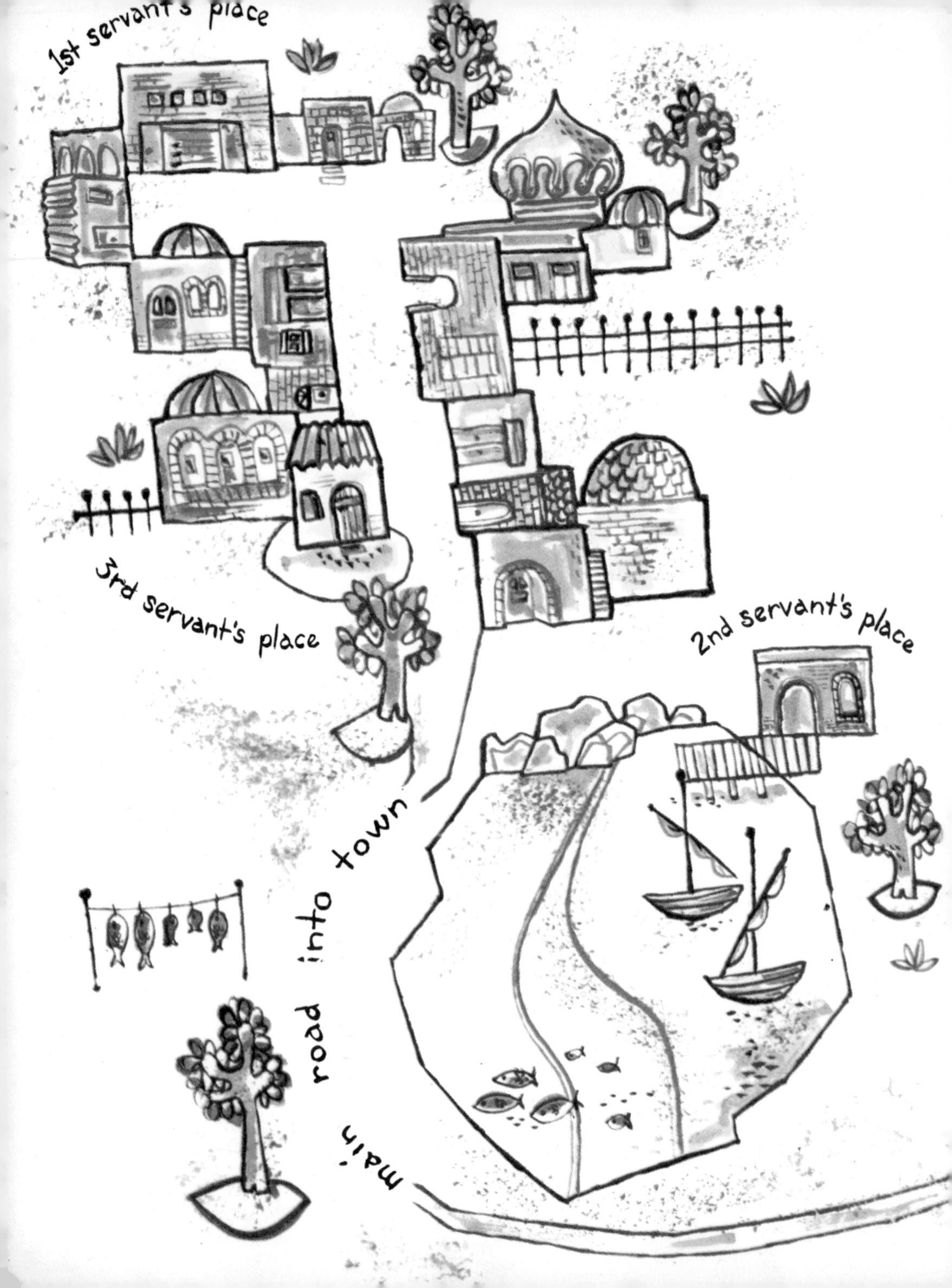
1st servant's place
3rd servant's place
2nd servant's place
main road into town

EIGHT BAGS OF GOLD

Written by Janice Kramer
Illustrated by Sally Mathews

MATTHEW 25:14-30 FOR CHILDREN

Concordia Publishing House St. Louis, Missouri

ARCH Books

CONCORDIA PUBLISHING HOUSE LTD., LONDON, W. C. 1
LIBRARY OF CONGRESS CATALOG CARD NO. 64-16985
MANUFACTURED IN THE UNITED STATES OF AMERICA

Once there was a master
well known throughout the land.
He had a hundred servants
who were under his command.

His house had many, many rooms,
and no one could deny
that he was rich, and there was not
a thing he couldn't buy.

One day the wealthy master
had important news to tell,
and so he called three servants
with a shiny silver bell.
The servants started running
when they heard the master's call;
until they reached the master's room,
they didn't stop at all.

They found the master waiting,
and they noticed at his side
a massive heap of precious gold
tied up in bags of hide.
"Ahem!" (The master cleared his throat.)
"I've called you here today
to tell you that I am about
to travel far away.

"The trip will be a long one,
so I think it's plain to see
that someone surely has to keep
these bags of gold for me.
I've thought and thought for many days,
and now I've hit upon
the answer to my problem —
YOU will keep them while I'm gone!"

He pointed to the servant
who was standing first in line:
"Come here," he said,
"and you shall have
your share of what is mine.
I give you these five bags of gold
to do with as you choose.
So then, till I return again,
these coins are yours to use."

Then to the second man he gave
two bags of gold and said:
"To make good use of all this wealth
you'll have to use your head."

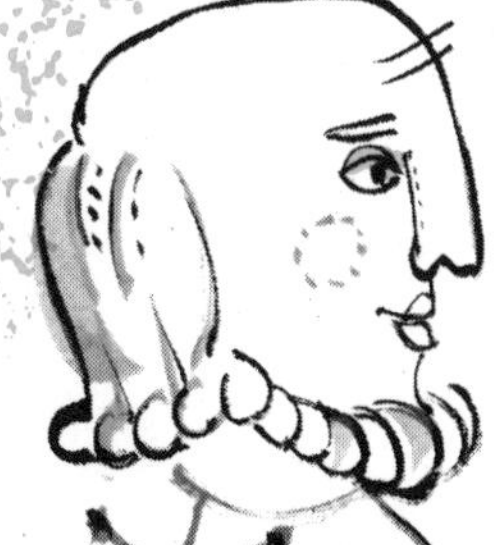

The servant who was last in line
approached the master's chair.
"There's one bag left," the master said,
"and that will be your share.

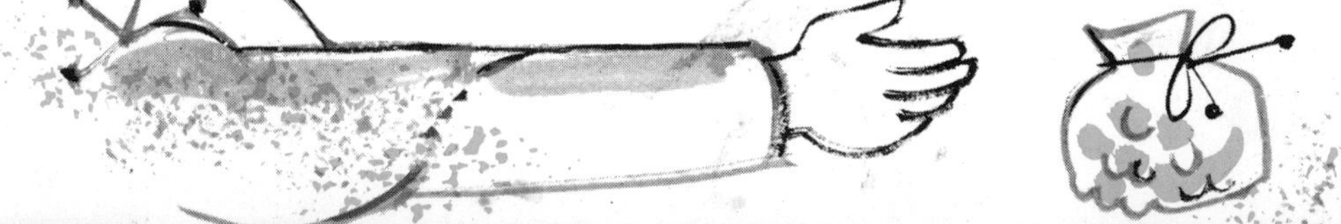

"Now go, but don't forget,
when I return, I'll want to see
what faithful stewards you have been
in using it for me."
The servants made a bow so low
their foreheads touched the floor,
and then they gathered up their gold
and headed for the door.

The man who had five bags of gold
went out with troubled thought,
and in his mind he counted up
the things that could be bought!
"It's such a task — I must not fail!"
the puzzled servant sighed,
but then a plan popped into mind.

"That's what I'll do!" he cried.

"I'll buy a store, a great big store—
I'll sell so many things!

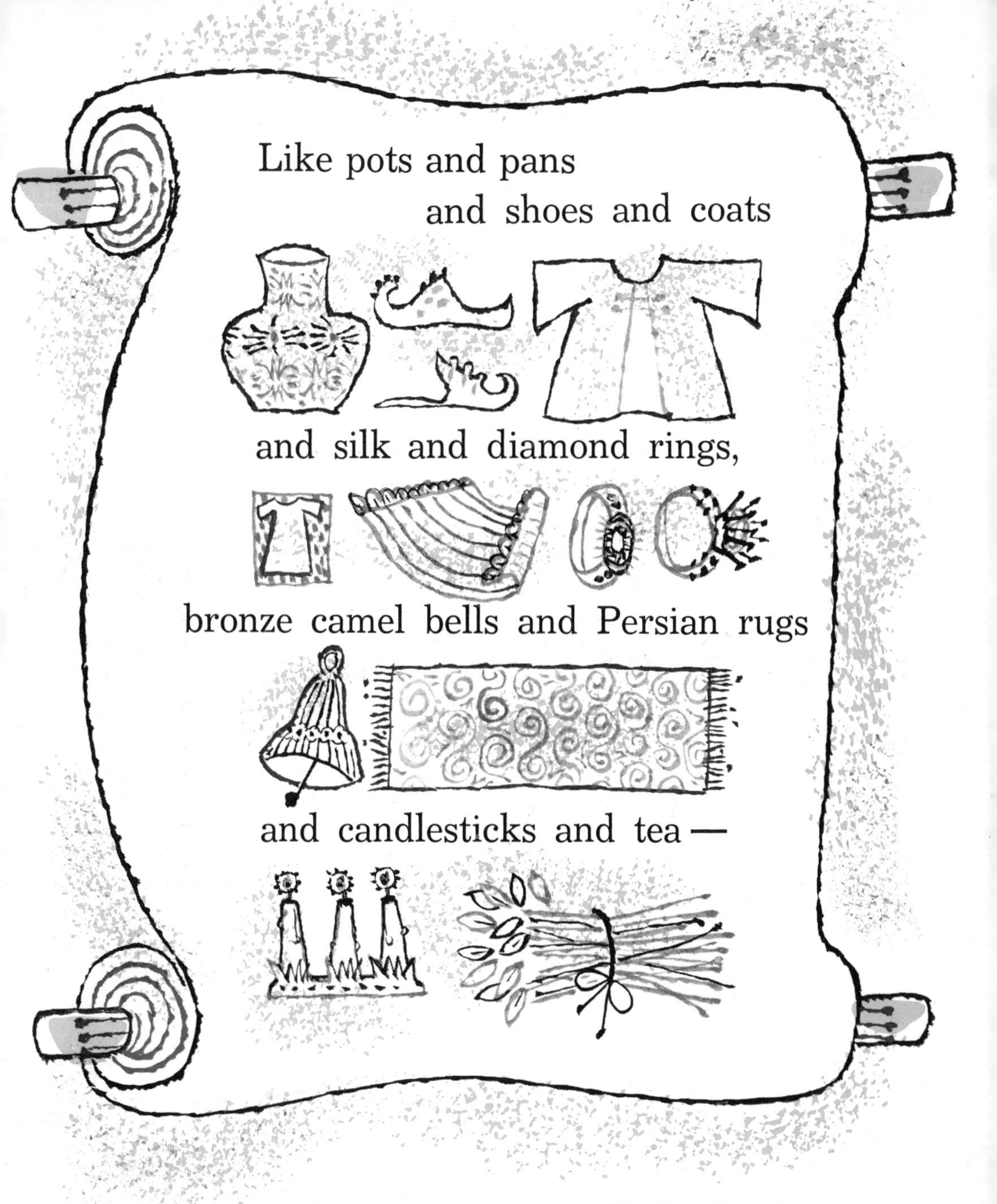

the biggest store in all the land,
that's what my store will be!"

He bought a store, and people came
from places all around;
they came from almost every place
where people could be found

to buy the things they needed
in this store that was so grand,
for it was soon the superstore,
the biggest in the land!

BIG STORE
SHOES
SPICES
SOAP
SALE!

And on the other side of town,
where shoreline meets the sea,
the man who had two bags of gold
was happy as could be.
For many years this servant
had possessed a secret wish:
to be the owner of a shop
for thriving trade in fish.

And so a marketplace for fish
was just the thing he bought,
and fishermen came in to sell him
all the fish they caught.

Then he in turn sold all the fish
to people of the land,
and so his business day by day
went on as he had planned.

For though he never had a crowd
around his little shed,
his marketplace did pretty well,
it truly must be said.
He didn't make a fortune
in his work of selling fish,
but still his marketplace fulfilled
his every dream and wish.

FISH FOR SALE

Now ever since his master
had departed on his way,
the man who had one bag of gold
had worried night and day.

"Oh, dear," he cried, "the gold I have
is such a small amount!
The coins my master gave to me
take little time to count.

"If I should use it — I might lose it! —
that would be the end!
I think he trusted it to me
to hide but not to spend."

And so that night he took his gold
and, quiet as a mouse,
he headed through the darkness
to an old, abandoned house.

FISH FOR SALE

Beneath the cellar floor he hid
the bag of gold secure.
"No one will ever find it here;
of that I can be sure."
Then up the stairs and through the door
into the night he ran.
"That spooky house," he panted,
"would sure scare the bravest men!"

The master then returned to town
and called his servants three:
"What have you done while I was gone?
I cannot wait to see."

The man who had received five bags
with pride stepped up and said,
"I bought a store, and now I have
ten bags of gold instead."

Then said the man who owned the shop
down by the ocean shore,
"You gave two bags of gold to me,
and I have gained two more."

"How wonderful!" the master said,
"and I am pleased to tell
you both that you shall have more gold
because you did so well!"

The man who had one bag of gold
came forward then and told
how he, to keep his treasure safe,
had hidden all his gold.
"Beneath the ground I buried it
and left it till today,
and here it is, the same amount
as when you went away."

"You foolish servant!" cried his lord,
as angry as could be.
"That you weren't brave with what you had
does not go well with me!

I wanted you to use it,
not hide it in a hole.
To do the best with what you had,
that should have been your goal."

The sad but wiser servant knew
he'd made a great mistake:
The master's gold was given
with a task to undertake.

His job was not to hide the gift
but use as best he could;
and if he failed, the master would
no doubt have understood.

Dear Parents:

This is a parable of Jesus.

It tells us that God expects us to make use of what He has given us in life.

He has given each of us different gifts. Some people can do things well with their hands, some with their heads, some with their voices; some can see things others don't.

Each of us is responsible to God for using the gifts he has from Him and for using them well.

In this parable Jesus gives encouragement to those who have gifts which seem small or few in comparison with the gifts others have. The master evidently had expected something even from the man with the one bag of gold. He was deeply disappointed that the servant had not even tried.

Can you help your child understand the meaning of the story? Will you help him also see and want to use the gifts God has given him and have confidence with regard to what he can do with them?

THE EDITOR